THE L

RE

"Stories are powers of reasons, but one reason is because they can provide indirect encouragement to live a certain way, follow a certain principle, be a certain kind of person. We've all heard the saying, 'The moral of the story is …' In this delightful book, Geoff Thomas draws out this principle from a number of American folktales, but with a big difference: he applies the moral in the story to Christ and the Christian life in surprising ways: some comparative, some contrastive—all creative! A most enjoyable read!"

Jonny Gibson, Associate Professor of Old Testament, Westminster Theological Seminary, Philadelphia; author of *The Moon Is Always Round*

"This is truly a unique book. I've never read another like it. Geoff Thomas has gathered both famous American folktales and historical vignettes and blended them with Gospel truths, all delivered in a way only a great Welsh storyteller and preacher like Geoff can tell them. Whether you are new to these stories or it's been years since you've read them, you'll enjoy encountering them in this classic collection."

Donald S. Whitney, Professor of Biblical Spirituality and Associate Dean, The Southern Baptist Theological Seminary, Louisville, KY; author of *Spiritual Disciplines for the Christian Life*, *Praying the Bible*, and *Family Worship*

"Everyone loves a story. A story with a lesson is far better than one with none. Biblical lessons are the best. Geoff Thomas is the consummate storyteller. Our children used to clamor, 'Tell us another one!' On these pages you'll find a fascinating mix of American folktales, with flavors from various nations. The bonus is the application—wisdom for everyday life and for eternal life. It's golden!"

Mary Beeke, wife of Joel Beeke, author of *Law of Kindness*

"It would diminish Geoff Thomas to call him a mere raconteur, even in connection with a book of stories. What elevates Geoff is his readiness to see God's truth revealed and reflected in the world God made, in both the virtues and the vices of his creatures. Here is a preacher, using fables and tales to make and to drive home spiritual points, showing himself both master and model."

Jeremy Walker, Pastor, Maidenbower Baptist Church

"There is no better way to teach about the human condition than by telling stories. Stories stick in our minds far better than theology does, which is why the Bible is filled with stories. Geoff Thomas has picked some fine old stories to re-tell to the next generation. Then he uses the Bible to evaluate them. His strategy works."

Gary North, Literature Teacher, grades 9–12, Ron Paul Curriculum

"As a dad of a sixteen year old I wish these stories had been available years ago. They are interesting, readable, funny and above all point to the Lord Jesus Christ. The author is one of my heroes. His preaching, example and writing have helped me enormously."

Alun Ebenezer, CEO & Executive Headmaster, Fulham Boys School

"These tall tales and adventures teach important life lessons as they point the reader to our Ultimate Example, the Lord Jesus Christ. Highly recommended for young and old to share together. Once you read the first story you will not want to stop! Read and enjoy!"

Mona Leiter, Mother, Grandmother, and Book Lover

"Geoff Thomas's affection for the cultural heritage of the United States finds expression in this delightful collection of American folktales, retold in his inimitable style. We find here all those winsome qualities that mark his preaching—the lush vocabulary of a master wordsmith, a colorful use of imagery and dialogue, a whimsical sense of humor, and a lyric expressiveness that seems to have sprung right out of the Welsh soil from which Geoff himself sprang! But above all, we find woven through these tales that golden thread which has been the central theme of Geoff's life—the gospel of our Lord Jesus Christ. With clarity and passion he calls his readers to know and love that adorable Savior whom he knows and has proclaimed for many years on both sides of the Atlantic."

Martin Rizley, Pastor, Grace Baptist Church, Málaga, Spain

ABOUT THE AUTHOR

Geoffrey Thomas was born in Merthyr Tydfil, Wales, in 1938. He studied at Cardiff University and later trained for the ministry at Westminster Theological Seminary, Philadelphia. He spent fifty years as Pastor of Alfred Place Baptist Church, Aberystwyth and is the author of several books and numerous articles. He has three other works of fiction forthcoming with Reformation Lightning. Geoffrey Thomas was awarded an honorary doctorate from Westminster Theological Seminary in 2011. He lives in London.

COMING SOON BY GEOFFREY THOMAS

ALSO BY REFORMATION LIGHTNING

The Emperor's New Clothes and Other Stories

The Pied Piper of Hamelin and Other Tales

The Boy Who Shouted "Wolf!" But There Wasn't A Wolf
and Other Fables

THE LEGENDARY CASEY JONES

AND OTHER AMERICAN FOLKTALES

GEOFFREY THOMAS

Reformation
Lightning

Reformation Lightning

www.reformationlightning.com

First published by Reformation Lightning in 2021

ISBN 978-1-8381883-0-6
1 3 5 7 10 8 6 4 2

To "The Brady Bunch"—
Rhodri, Dylan, Dewi, Gwion and Owain

CONTENTS

AMERICAN FOLKTALES

This book is full of American folktales—good stories that one generation passes on to another. All richly human and soaked in the influence that the Bible has had in North America for five hundred years.

Christianity has given Americans the ideals of redeeming grace, forgiveness and new life. It has also taught them that the great aim of humanity is to glorify and enjoy the living God, to love our neighbours as ourselves, to resist temptations to hurt others and to overcome evil by doing good.

These things have saturated and structured the wonderful freedoms of the United States throughout its history to today. The Christian church has contributed psalms, hymns and the pattern of meeting together once a week. It has defined and encouraged family life, of parents nurturing and teaching their children, telling them their stories and describing their heritage.

Folktales go back to an agricultural age, to an acquaintance with wild animals: deer, rabbits, foxes, cougars, racoons, buffalos, beavers and bears. The stories reflect the presence of Native Americans, African Americans, Latinos, Chicanos and Canadians who all have injected their own stories into the mix of the continent's folklore.

North American folktales have homespun humour by the bucketful. They are less bloodthirsty and far less cruel than many of the stories gathered in Germany by the Brothers Grimm, but European fairy tales have had a pervasive effect on the population of the United States through its millions of immigrants. They are all part of the incredible mix of the nation's folklore.

In this book you will find larger than life historical personalities, nostalgia, quaintness and cuteness, but also inspiration and encouragement to consider afresh the rich achievements of individuals who have come to acknowledge Jesus Christ as their Lord and God.

BEWARE OF THE WORDS, SMILES AND FROWNS OF MEN

There are many people in the world who want you to put your trust in them.

"Believe what I tell you!" they cry.

"Give me your support!"

"Back me!"

"See how clever I am!"

"I've got it!"

"I've arrived!"

"Don't you want what I've got?"

"Follow me and then you and I will both have a wonderful future!"

There was once a farmer who was given a fine piece of iron as payment for building a fence right around a neighbour's farm. He was pleased with the bargain as in his days iron was very scarce. He kept it safe while he wondered what he would buy with it.

A year or two passed and then he heard that a new blacksmith had come to the local village. So one morning he saddled his horse and rode over the hill and to the valley bottom. He forded the river standing on his stirrups on the back of his horse as it swam through the centre of the torrent. Then he rode the stallion down the bank for another mile until he came to the village and to the new smith. A curl of smoke came out of the chimney and so the farmer knew that the smith was busy. He dismounted and tied his horse to the hitching rail. He picked up the heavy piece of iron from the saddlebag and carried it into the forge.

"Good morning, neighbour!" said the blacksmith.

"Good morning, friend!" said the farmer. "How's business?"

"Yes, I'm doing great," said the blacksmith.

But the farmer noticed that the forge was the cleanest he had ever seen. There did not seem much evidence of work being done. Still, he spoke to the smith and said, "I need an axe. There are a number of trees that need to be cut down and I have this piece of iron. Can you make an axe head for me?"

"Of course I can," said the blacksmith. "Come

back Tuesday afternoon and I will have it ready for you."

"I am mighty glad to hear it," the farmer said and shook hands with the smith and went out and untied his horse and rode out of the village and along the river bank for a mile. Then he forded the river and went up and up over the steep hill, down the other side and home another mile where he entered his log cabin and told his wife the good news.

On Tuesday afternoon, after he had eaten a dish of gumbo, the farmer saddled his horse and rode it to the hill and climbed up and up to the top in the rain and down the other side slipping and sliding until he got to the river. It was deeper than before, but his horse was strong and they forded the river together. Then down the riverside lane they went until they came to the village and the blacksmith's shop. The farmer tethered the horse and entered the smithy.

"Hello friend," he said, and greeted the blacksmith. "How have you got on with my axe head?"

"Oh," the smith said. "There wasn't enough metal to make an axe."

"Not enough? I reckon there was plenty and some spare."

"Not at all. The metal shrinks when you heat it white hot."

"Oh? I've never heard that in all my life."

"But I tell you what I can do," said the smith. "I can make you a fine hammer."

"Well, I do need a hammer," said the disappointed farmer. "All right, do that."

So he went out of the forge and untethered his horse and rode it out of the village, along the riverbank, across the swiftly flowing river and up the steep slippery hill, carefully down the other side, and finally the last mile home to the log cabin to tell his wife of his disappointment.

The next afternoon he set out again after he had finished another bowl of gumbo. He rode to the bottom of the hill, and along the narrow path through the trees, and up and up until he reached the crest of the hill. Then down and down they went slipping and brushing through the wet trees and bushes until they reached the river. The horse hesitated, but the farmer urged it on and across the river they went, the horse swimming for a while. Along the riverbank path they rode to the village and up to the smithy where he tethered his horse and ducked his head under the wide doorway and entered the forge.

"Hello neighbour!" he said. "How have you got on making my hammer?"

The blacksmith frowned. "What you gave me would never make a hammer. It is much too small."

"Too small?" replied the farmer. "To me it seems plenty big enough for two hammers at least."

"Ah, you don't understand the work of a blacksmith. When you heat the iron up red hot it shrinks. But I can make you a fine screwdriver."

"A screwdriver?" cried the farmer. "A screwdriver!"

"Or a small chisel," said the blacksmith hurriedly.

"A little chisel!" cried the farmer, thinking of all the work he had done in building the fences around his neighbour's farm.

"Take it or leave it," said the big burly blacksmith looking down at him with unsmiling eyes.

"I'll come back for it tomorrow afternoon," the unhappy farmer muttered.

The farmer went out, untied the knot on the horse's rein, mounted and made the long journey home as the sun was setting, riding alongside the river, across the swiftly flowing torrent, up the steep wet hill, sliding down the path on the other side, and along to the lights of home, where he poured out his disappointment and frustration to his sympathetic wife.

The next afternoon, after eating the gumbo that he always ate for dinner, he saddled his horse and off he went to the hill and down to the river and across the torrent and down the riverbank to the village and the smithy. He tethered his horse and went into the forge wondering what tall tale he would get today from the blacksmith.

The bearded man in his leather apron turned around and looked at him.

"Well," said the farmer, "is my chisel ready?"

"No, there wasn't enough iron for a chisel or a screwdriver. But I have this for you." And he put his hand into the trough of water alongside the fire and drew out a nail which he gave to the farmer. "That was all I could get out of that piece of iron you gave me."

"You said you would make an axe head, and now all you have given me is a nail!"

"Well that is the reality of the iron industry," said the tall, mean-faced blacksmith. "Hot iron shrinks. Be glad you have something," he said, before adding, "and that will be five dollars."

The farmer laughed and laughed. He turned his back on the blacksmith and threw the nail onto the floor. He walked out of the smithy and rode home to tell his wife the sorry tale.

"But I didn't pay that rogue a penny," he said, "and when I go to the market next week I will tell every farmer there about the blacksmith with all his promises, none of which he kept. Not another farmer will go to him. He won't be a blacksmith in our area much longer. He talks the talk, but he doesn't walk the walk."

Don't be hoodwinked by words, and don't be bought by people's smiles. Do you know that the Lord Jesus Christ never once hoodwinked people with his words. When he told people about the way, the truth and the life he made it obvious that he was talking about himself. When he told people what it meant to have eternal life, he told them they got it by believing in him. When he told them how to have rest, it was through coming to him. And every word he spoke was true.

"You believe in God," he said, "then also believe in me."

He told people he was going to die but that he would rise from the dead. He did die on a cross, but on the third day, just as he had said, he rose from the dead and spent forty days talking, walking, eating and drinking with others until he returned to heaven.

He never lies.

He never hoodwinks.

———————

Let me tell you another story. There was once a gentleman who never spoke to any individual or a crowd of people without a wide smile. He had a mesmerising effect on people and everyone he spoke to would smile back at him and nod their heads at what he said.

He discovered the power of his grin when he was a teenager. He smiled at the bullies in the school and they didn't punch him—even though they wanted to. He smiled at all the girls and they went out with him. He smiled at any teacher when he did not bring his work to school on time. He smiled at the cows in the field when he opened the gate and they all walked to the barn without needing a dog to snap at their heels. He smiled at the sheep when he needed them to move from the High Meadow to the Oak Tree Meadow and no sheep dogs were needed to bring in the stragglers. He simply smiled and they obeyed.

He found that the way to get his own way was by

smiling. He could do anything by the power of his grinning face. His power over his mother and father was enormous and he became an utterly spoiled child. He got everything he wanted by the seduction of his smiles.

Then one day he was walking home through the woods and he saw a squirrel high up in a tree and he smiled at it. The squirrel did not budge. He screwed up his eyes and focused all his energy on the squirrel and grinned and grinned until his face ached. There was not one ounce of movement in the animal and the boy's anger grew and grew.

He stalked home and got his father's saw and axe and returned to the tree where the squirrel was. He began to chop down the tree. He glanced up at the animal but it remained high up on its branch. He cut a deep section out of the trunk and then went to the other side and sawed and sawed until blisters appeared on his hands, his arms ached and he grew weary with the task.

Then finally there was a movement and a sound and the tree began to crack and lean and with increasing speed it fell, crashing onto the forest floor. He walked up to the treetop to see what had happened to the squirrel. He hoped that it had been crushed in the fall—his anger at the defying creature had intensified through the hour of sawing and chopping. How dare it resist his smile?

But he could not see a squirrel. Instead there was a curved bushy branch, just like a squirrel's tail, and in front of it a broken branch with a knob of wood at the top and two dots exactly like a pair of eyes. There was never a squirrel there. It was just a branch of wood that looked so uncannily like a squirrel and all his effort had been for nothing. He could not grin the bark off a tree.

The boy had to learn what we all must learn, that it is with truth, integrity, kindness and trust that we gain the respect and support of our neighbours. How foolish to believe a man and support him by giving him our faith simply because we've been bought by his smile.

———

Do you know that Jesus never won anyone by his smiles? He was the happiest man that this world has ever seen. He was full of joy. Through his life he daily learned to be content with whatever God brought him.

But we are not told that he charmed people into following him by constantly smiling at them. In fact we are told that when the people of Jerusalem would not come to him for his truth and his protection he wept and wept.

"Oh Jerusalem," he cried, "I would have spread my wings over you and protected you from the hungry cruel hawks and eagles that would swoop down on you, but you smiled at one another, and you said, 'Sorry! We don't need you Jesus. We don't need your protection. We can save ourselves. Don't cry for *us*, Jesus!'"

They resisted his invitations and all his promises of rest, truth and protection. They would not come to the happiest man in the world, the one who was God the Son, and they died without him and their beautiful city, Jerusalem, was destroyed within one generation. They lost their souls and gained death. But I have one more word of warning.

There was once a man who realised that he had come from a frowning family and they had programmed him to shake his head just like them. He pursed his lips just like them and expressed his disapproval by shaking his head at anything that displeased him, just as they did. There was very little laughter in his home. His parents never kissed good-bye.

When he had asked why they didn't do what his friends did, the answer he got was, "Well, we have never done it like that."

He copied all that his frowning mother and disapproving father used to say and echoed their every opinion.

His father snarled the word "Capitalism!" often and so his son said the same, not knowing what it meant.

He was fourteen going on forty and when he was eighteen he was going on eighty.

When he walked past a cinema he said to his friends, "That is a bad place."

If they said words like "blinking" or "bloomin'" or "shucks" then he would say, "You shouldn't say that. It's a bad word."

He said that the President was a bad man. Any change in the worship services on Sundays was bad. They just went once on a Sunday. He told anyone who went to church twice that they were "extreme." The family never went to meetings during the week, and they disapproved of men who stood in the street and preached or gave out tracts. His father said the Salvation Army was "men playing soldiers." He believed anything new was bound to result in losing everything. The food they ate was very plain. They always went on vacation to the same Bed and Breakfast in a side street far from the beach for a week once a year. They had a television set but they never watched sports. They didn't have a dog or cat because they thought it was a waste of money. Their car was very old and frequently broke down.

Eventually the boy went to university. It was a difficult time for him. He didn't make any friends. He sat by himself and walked by himself and hated most of life there. He even found the Chess Club a little shocking. He called home every day and every two weeks his parents came to visit him.

But it was at university that a great change came into his life. There was a group of students in his hall of residence that were different. When they ate together he noticed how they bowed their heads and one of them gave thanks for the food. They were happy and often laughed. They smiled at him and one day he was invited by them to one of their meetings.

He had stopped going to church when he left home and when he sat in this meeting he had never experienced anything like it. He had never heard anyone, except the minister in the pulpit, say prayers. These students prayed, both men and women, and they talked about Jesus Christ in a very familiar and sweet way as if they knew him. They gave him a book to read and what was written in it gripped him.

He went back to the meetings each week because he was lonely and they always spoke to him and made him welcome. He did not know that they were praying for him to trust in Jesus Christ as his Lord and Saviour. He did not tell his parents what he was doing because he knew they would disapprove.

Then one day he was impacted by a speaker who told the students the meaning of Christianity: that Christians have come by the grace of God to realise that they have failed to love God and not love their neighbours as themselves. When, in the past, they judged others for how they lived they were also judging themselves. They deserved eternal death because they were sinners, but Jesus Christ, because he loved them, had died in their place and risen from the dead. The one great reason people should become Christians is that it was true. Jesus rose from the dead on the third day, and it was true. If anyone comes to him then he will not cast them out but give them rest.

It's true!

That night he spoke to God for the first time and the next day he knew that a change had taken place in his life. He had a new peace and a joy. As the weeks went by his hypocrisy and judgmental spirit grew weaker. It did not disappear entirely though, and some of the things he said made his new friends tease him.

They said, "It's fine if you don't want to do things or go to certain places, but you must show us in the Bible if something is wrong for us too so that we can change how we live. We want to please God in everything we do."

Oh, he thought. I'm a bit judgmental aren't I?

And then he read in the Bible the words of Jesus, "Don't judge or you yourself will be judged."

He finally met a girl among those Christians and he fell in love with her, and she showed much patience and kindness to him and she, as much as anyone, was the one who liberated him from his frowns and ready expressions of disapproval about everything and anything. He learned to laugh at himself while still respecting his parents and he prayed for them. In fact they were impressed with the change that had taken place in his life and did not express their disapproval that he changed churches and went to his new church twice on a Sunday and once during the week.

The Lord Jesus was a wonderful encourager. The one group of people he denounced were the Pharisees who were so judgmental and critical of anyone who was not like them. He told them that they were like white tombstones, reflecting the sunshine on their white marble, but underneath those stones were dead bodies rotting away.

The Lord encouraged his disciples.

"You are the salt of the earth," he said to those young and inexperienced men. "You are the light of the world!"

They must have looked at one another in amazement. They were so shallow and ignorant. They wanted fame, and they didn't understand him, nor did they want him to die and rise again, though that was the point of him coming into the world.

When Jesus' enemies came to arrest him they all ran away and hid so that he was alone.

One of them, Judas, betrayed him and another, Peter, denied ever knowing him. But he had compassion on Peter and forgave him and made him a great spokesman and preacher.

Jesus was not a man that shook his head every day and disapproved at the behaviour of everyone he met. His patience and forgiveness and mercy outweighed the sins of others. Aren't you glad that you can come to such a kind and merciful Lord and ask him to give you rest?

We have looked at three examples of people being influenced by others. The first was a farmer who believed a blacksmith who told him that "certainly he would help him," but all he told him was untrue. Don't believe everyone's words. Take care as they make their big promises.

The second man bought people by his smiles. Be careful of people who tell you that they are happy and have everything and don't need saving.

The third couple intimidated their son by their disapproval of everything. They were prisoners by their own laws and ideas. They judged everyone and disapproved of everybody else but never of themselves.

Such people are all around us but we can be delivered from them—from liars and smilers and strict rule-followers—and that salvation comes to us when we make Jesus Christ our Lord, and trust in his life of righteousness and his sacrifice as the Lamb of God. He gave himself to deliver us from the fear and captivity of sin. When you serve him then you know a life of happy freedom.

BRER FOX, BRER RABBIT AND THE
TWO FAILURES

There once lived in the same wood a fox and a rabbit. It's right to say at the beginning that neither character is very likeable. Both are a couple of failures. One was always angry and the other was always a smarty-pants. One was always a flop, and the other was always smug and pleased with himself and so, really, he was just another kind of failure. It is hard to like either of them. You wouldn't want either to be your friend. Let me give you an example of how Brer Fox and Brer Rabbit behaved to one another.

One day Brer Rabbit was quietly hopping along eating a fresh carrot for supper, not on his guard, not watching for anyone who would like to eat him up. Then from behind a tree trunk out dived Brer Fox and grabbed him good and firm. He really got Brer Rabbit so that he couldn't move. He pinned him down on the ground and put his nose an inch away from Brer Rabbit's nose and opened his mouth and breathed all over his face.

He said, "Gotcha, at last. Gotcha! Gotcha! Gotcha! Now I know what I'm having for supper tonight. Ha! Ha! Ha! At last! You are never getting away from me again. Never, never, never!"

And he licked his lips and his yellow teeth and laughed with triumph, remembering the many times Brer Rabbit had escaped him and humiliated him so that all the animals in the wood had laughed about Brer Rabbit's latest tactic in triumphing over his oldest enemy Brer Fox.

Brer Rabbit quickly composed himself.

"I was looking for you," he said. "I had something exciting to tell you."

"No, no, no!" said Brer Fox. "I have heard your stories a hundred times. This is the end. Good-bye Brer Rabbit! I can't say that it's been good to know you because it hasn't. No more tall tales from you!"

"Okay, okay," said the rabbit. "If you don't want to hear about the lemonade spring then that's your loss."

"The lemonade spring?" said Brer Fox slowly. "What do you mean?"

"I just went around the very edge of the forest and discovered where a spring of lemonade runs into the lake. It is so delicious and I was on my way back so very slowly, to tell all the animals about it, and I wasn't thinking about anything else, my tummy is full of the most delicious lemonade."

If there was one thing that Brer Fox loved more than anything else, then it was lemonade. Wow! He could drink a whole bottle without stopping and then he would sleep and sleep with the most marvellous dreams.

"Take me there now," he said, not letting go of Brer Rabbit.

"Well, okay," the rabbit replied.

They went deep into the wood where it was quite dark and few animals lived there.

"No, it's further on," he would tell Brer Fox as he grew weary of carrying Brer Rabbit.

"If you're telling me a lie than you will die very, very slowly," said the fox to the rabbit.

"What me? Tell a lie? It is not much further."

On they walked out of the wood to the side of the big blue lake. They walked along the bank until they came to a little creek with a muddy bottom.

"You see that spring running out of the bank? That

is the purest, sweetest lemonade you have ever tasted in your life. I can smell it from here."

Brer Fox sniffed the air and thought he could smell it.

"You could make a fortune selling drinks from that spring, in yellow bottles, 'Lakeside Lemonade,' half-dime a bottle!"

Brer Fox filled his mind with thoughts of a stall and a banner and a long line of animals waiting to get lemonade, and without thinking he began to loosen his grip on Brer Rabbit. He thought of all the money he would earn from the 'Lakeside Lemonade.'

"Now you have to jump down here, right off the bank. That is the shortest way to the spring."

With a great leap Brer Fox jumped off the bank, and landed in quicksand that started to swallow him up. He let go of Brer Rabbit as he sank up to his middle in the mud, but Brer Rabbit was much lighter than Brer Fox and he lay on the surface with his four legs stretched out and he swam and paddled along the top of the quicksand to the bank and then sat on the top watching Brer Fox slowly slip deeper and deeper into the mud.

"Help! Help me!" he cried. "Do something Brer Rabbit. Help me. Please help me. I will never touch you again."

Brer Rabbit laughed. "I have heard that before. You'll still want me for your supper. You always will."

"No, no, never again!" cried the fox as the cold stream chilled his stomach and the mud sucked him further down.

"Okay, let me tell you something," said Brer Rabbit. "The mud's not that deep and at any moment your feet should touch the rock."

And with that Brer Fox stopped thrashing about. He had reached the bottom of the mud and he breathed a sigh of relief. He was not going to die. That terrible rabbit! Brer Fox began to push his way slowly through the sticky goo to the bank as Brer Rabbit laughed at him.

"I'll get you, you varmint," Brer Fox snarled at Brer Rabbit as he got nearer and nearer the bank.

"We'll see about that," said the rabbit, and as the stinking muddy fox clambered out of the creek Brer Rabbit trotted off, glancing back and laughing at the fox. He was always faster than Brer Fox who was in no condition to run after him with his red coat caked in the gooiest mud that he had ever experienced.

"How can I get him? How can I get him?" the fox fumed to himself as he washed in the lake and picked the mud out of his fine red coat. Humiliated again by Brer Rabbit.

It was not long before Brer Fox thought of another way of catching Brer Rabbit. It came to him as he watched a mouse struggling as it was stuck in some tar at the edge of the hot water springs. With their pools of blue water, where no fish could survive, and the geysers that sent occasional columns of water into the air, there, around the edges of the little ponds, were bubbling pools of tar, and they gave Brer Fox a brilliant idea. He gathered a load of tar into two buckets and carried them back to the path through the old woods. He quickly made a large doll out of the tar. He put a pretty straw hat on its head and sat it in the shade near the path, not far from Brer Rabbit's home.

For an hour Brer Fox hid near the big patch of briers where, in the late summer, children would come to pick blackberries. Then along from his burrow came Brer Rabbit feeling very pleased with himself waving at the squirrels and nodding at Brer Badger, whistling a happy rabbit song. Then he noticed the stranger sitting near the path with a lovely hat on their head.

"Good morning, friend," he cried.

Nothing. Not a twitch.

"Good morning, travelling friend," he shouted out.

Again zilch. No response at all.

"What an ill-mannered creature," he thought. He got very close and coughed but the head did not move.

"Not feeling well are we? A little deaf are we? How are you today, friend?"

But the person ignored him, and Brer Rabbit blew his top.

"You ignorant son of a gun!" he shouted out and gave it a blow on its hat. But the hat didn't move and the rabbit found his elbow was stuck on the black doll's shoulder. And when he pushed to free it with his other arm then that arm became stuck in the chest of this ... horrible mannequin. He kicked at it in his fear and rage and his foot stuck fast and he fell over. Poor Brer Rabbit with the tar doll inseparably united to him.

Then, so coolly and slowly, Brer Fox sauntered across to him from his hiding place near the brier patch.

"Good morning, friend!" he said to him imitating the very words that Brer Rabbit had spoken to the tar doll.

The rabbit said nothing, inwardly fuming that he had fallen into Brer Fox's trap.

"Oh!" said the fox. "Are we too 'stuck up' to speak to anyone this morning?"

Brer Rabbit struggled to free himself but the more he struggled the faster he got stuck in the tar doll.

"Well, I know what I am having for dinner today," Brer Fox said, carefully grabbing hold of Brer Rabbit and pulling him free from the big lump of tar. "Now what shall I have with you in my pot? I will put in some carrots and leeks and peas and beans and celery and a tomato. That sounds so good, but first I think a little pain after all the pain you have given me is required. The chickens at last have come home to roost!"

"Oh Brer Fox, I understand exactly how you feel. If I were standing where you stand now then I would feel the same. If you want to hang me then hang me. If you want to drop me into your boiling pot then drop me in. If you want to cut me open then do that too. But one thing I plead with you not to do and that is to throw me into that horrible brier patch. Please, any of the other things, be my guest, but one place I cannot stand in the whole world is that horrid brier patch. Anything except that. Please, please, please Brer Fox, for the sake of my mother, and your mother, don't afflict me by tossing me into the frightful brier patch. You will not live with your conscience when you hear me scream with pain as I land there. No one, not even me, is bad enough to endure such a fate. The pot. The knife. The rope. Any of those, even all of those, but please, please, please, not the brier patch."

Brer Fox's eyes gleamed with delight. His great enemy that had made his name a laughing stock was in his power at last, and here was a fate worse than all the other ways of dying that he could inflict upon Brer Rabbit.

"You have humiliated me and made me look like a clown to everyone in the wood. You have made a fool of me and every animal I see mocks and sniggers at me. You varmint! There is only one place good enough for you ..."

And with that he pulled back his arm and threw Brer Rabbit high into the air and into the middle of the brier patch.

Then Brer Fox waited for blood-curdling screams, but there was none. He waited for any sound at all, but there was nothing, and the longer the silence the more worried Brer Fox became. He had thought that he was going to cause Brer Rabbit great suffering by throwing Brer Rabbit into a torture chamber, not into a bed of silence.

"Has that rogue tricked me again?" he sighed.

"Hello! Hello!" came a voice that he knew only too well, and there, on a little hill looking down at him and pulling lumps of tar out of his fur coat was Brer

Rabbit. "I'm afraid that I got you again Brer Fox," he said. "Didn't you know that I was born in a brier patch and lived the first years of my life in a brier patch, and that I love brier patches. They give me shade in the summer and protection in the winter. Think of my name "Brer Rabbit." Doesn't it sound to you like brier patch? Brer and brier and brier and brer. Thank you so much for delivering me to my old home. You are a very kind fox indeed."

"Aaaaaaaaaah!" screamed Brer Fox in his frustration. "Whenever will I be able to catch that sly, crafty, cunning animal?" He shook his fist at the rabbit, "You wait! You just wait Brer Rabbit. I'll get you."

But Brer Rabbit simply smiled and waved and disappeared over the hill.

How different was the Lord Jesus! There were groups of men who came to him and provoked him with silly questions, but he answered them quietly, truthfully and tenderly. He would not get angry with them and curse them for their foolishness. They finally showed their hatred to him by nailing him to a cross and hanging him there until he died. But his first words about them were in a prayer that his heavenly Father would forgive them for their ignorance. He could have become so furious with them, but his words were, "Come to me, all of you who are weary and burdened, and I will give you rest." He told his enemies that he longed to spread out his wings over them and protect them, and he told us that we should love our enemies, and bless those who curse us, and pray for those who hurt us.

Weren't Brer Fox and Brer Rabbit foolish creatures to be scheming and fighting and threatening and tricking one another?

Do you know that the Spirit who filled the Lord Jesus can fill you too if you speak to Jesus and tell him that you don't want to be angry or bitter or always trying to beat other people. You ought to live patient and forgiving lives. Ask him to make you live like that and he will help you change and give you a strong heart of growing kindness and love. That is the best gift of all, not that you get the last word and are more clever than everyone else.

THE BATTLE OF THE BRAGGARTS

There was once a group of good-old-boys who were sitting on the banks of the mighty Mississippi chewing the cud. One man boasted to the others that he could brag better than anyone else in America.

"No you can't," said another man, just as foolish as the first man. "I can brag better than you and better than anyone in the whole world."

"What nonsense!" cried the first man, "I can brag far better than you."

All the men got excited, their slumber vanishing. They cried for a competition to take place, laying bets on who would win this stupidity.

"Both of you must brag and we will judge who is the best," they decided.

"Stop! This is a lot of nonsense," said a little

fellow with a black beard, but everyone else mocked him and told him to shut up. They wanted their fun. So the first man began.

"Stand back! Give me room! I can walk like an ox, jump like a frog, run like a deer, hunt like a wolf, charge like a buffalo, swim like an eel, fly like an eagle and stink like a skunk. I am the original iron-jawed son of Arkansas. Look at me! My father was a hurricane and my mother was an earthquake! I eat eighteen alligators for breakfast and sixty pounds of rattlesnakes for supper! I can split a granite rock just by glancing at it. The thunder grows silent when I speak. Cast a glance at me, gentlemen. But quickly lower your eyes and hold your breath because soon I'll tell you some things about myself that will make you tremble."

Then he jumped up and clicked his heels together three times and walked around the seated men leaning over and breathing into the faces of each one.

"Don't you try looking at me with your naked eyes. Don't you know that I use the lightning to scratch my back? And in the summer I go for my vacation to the Gulf of Mexico and I hunt whales from dawn to dusk and I've caught a hundred in a single day. When I am thirsty I reach up and grab a cloud as a cold-water sponge and suck it dry. When I am hot I clap my hands and a soft wind blows and cools my cheeks. I can put my hand on the sun's face and its rays don't burn my skin. If I am hungry then I bite a piece of cheese off the moon. When I shake myself the Rocky Mountains tremble."

And he jumped up and down triumphantly. No one could boast like he could.

Then his opponent got up and walked towards him. They faced each other and walked round and round one another, glaring and mocking, punching the air.

The other began, "I have never heard such nonsense in my life! You call that bragging? Why, you don't know a bee from a buffalo's foot! You ain't heard nothin' yet!"

Both men were growling, getting near to the other and then passing by, turning and approaching the other again and again full of spite and threats. Then the second braggart began.

"I was born in the swamps of Louisiana, half horse and half snapping turtle. I can wade across the Mississippi in two minutes. I can ride a flash of lightning. I can turn a big black bear inside out in a moment; I just grab his tongue and pull. I can out-shoot, out-run, out-jump, out-brag, out-fight any man on either side of the Mississippi. Come on you flatterers! Come on you spectators, come on you doubters and see if what I am saying is true!

"I can beat any boxer five times my weight in any place two thousand miles from here in any direction. All the men of Chicago tremble and run when I arrive in the windy city. I will walk ten miles, day or night, for someone to fight. When I was born I refused my mother's offer of milk to drink. 'Give me gumbo and turnip greens,' I said to her. When I go riding then a single horse will never do for me. I always ride two stallions. I can pull a giant redwood tree out of the ground with my bare arms. When I live on the mountaintops I eat the thunder. When I live in the valley bottoms I drink the river dry. I can stop a train with my mighty body. I can out-ride, out-run, out-swim, out-jump, out-sing, out-throw, out-shoot, out-toss, out-climb, out-roar anyone or anything on this planet.

"I once slid down a desert cactus with a mountain lion under each arm and never felt a thing. Grizzly bears plead for mercy when they see me coming. I'm the wildest, toughest fighter in the West. When I'm hungry I bite the nose off a grizzly bear. I live in a box canyon, and everyone who lives there is wild, and the further up that canyon you walk the wilder the people who live there are, and I live at the very end!"

Then he burst into a song and jig:

> *"I'm Colossus from the prairies way out in the*
> *West;*
> *I'm sheet lightning—I do not speak in jest.*
> *If you want to die of terror then cast a glance*
> *at me.*
> *All the buffalos are mine on the boundless*
> *prairie."*

He finished by saying, "I am a man; I have the best horse, best dog, best land, best gun, best sons and the handsomest wife in all of Mississippi."

All the men hooted and shouted in their response to this nonsense and they announced that he was the winner. He'd bragged better than the first man, but the two men weren't angry with one another. They began to walk away arm in arm and laughing when suddenly the little man with the black beard spoke up again.

"You spoke folly ... both of you ... you spoke out of turn ... you went too far and you need to be taught a lesson so that you don't talk like that ever again."

The two men glanced at one another and stopped and walked slowly and deliberately back towards him.

"And who is going to teach us that lesson?"

"I suppose that's going to be me," he said.

As they laughed and strolled towards him with their fists raised and eyes narrowed he suddenly shot forward and with two mighty blows knocked each one out stone cold, leaving them lying still on the ground. He looked at the men sitting round staring in amazement at what they had just seen.

"God alone can speak of himself. We only have what he gives," he said as quietly he walked away back to his home.

The little man with the black beard should not have hit the men but he was right in what he said.

Think of Jesus. He never bragged, and if there was anyone who had things to boast about it would have been the carpenter's son from Nazareth. But he never opened his mouth in order to draw attention to his mighty acts. He was meek like a lamb. But then he made such extraordinary claims. He remained lowly in his lifestyle and yet he made a number of breath-taking statements.

The Lord Jesus said that one day all the world would have to stand before him and he would tell all men and women where all of them were going to spend eternity. In other words, he is going to judge the world. Christ is going to sit on God's throne and he will decide the destinies of all of us. It is not that he is going to judge one nation, or one period of human history, but all of us are going to meet our Judge and hear his judgment of us.

We live in a moral universe and whatever we sow we will harvest. When you put a bean behind blotting paper inside a glass jar and fill it with sawdust and water then the seed soon starts to sprout and to put down roots and put up shoots. It does not produce oranges and bananas. It produces beans. Whatever you sow you will harvest. If you sow a life of contempt for the Lord Jesus Christ you reap the fruit of judgment on yourself.

But our Lord makes an even more astonishing claim. He says that the standards by which we are going to be judged are very specific. They are how we respond to him! If we don't love him, he is going to say, "I never knew you." In other words the decisive thing, the Lord Christ says, in your destiny, is whether Jesus loved you with a saving love or not. What is your relationship with the Son of God? Are you proud of Jesus Christ and unashamed of him and his words?

Or, again, how do you respond to the people who

love and serve our Lord? Jesus Christ says that he will welcome those who loved and helped his people. Those who fed and clothed his disciples. Those who go to prisons where Christ's people are locked away for telling the world about him. Your relationship with Jesus Christ and his people, or your neglect of them, is going to be the standard by which you will be judged.

Or, again, the Lord Jesus Christ makes another claim, that he existed before he entered the womb of his mother Mary. He said, "Before Abraham was I am." Abraham lived two thousand years before Christ but our Lord said he was a living person before Abraham. He was in the beginning with God. In fact he never began. There never was a time when Jesus did not exist.

But even more than that astonishing claim, the Lord Jesus Christ stated that he was God. He said, "I and my Father are one." It does not matter where you read about Jesus in the Bible, in the Old Testament, in the Gospels of Matthew, Mark, Luke and John, in the letters of Paul and Peter, or in the book of Revelation. Everywhere you look you meet a Christ who is God. He is the one who made the universe and he is the one who sustains and maintains it. Our breath is in his hands. He will bring the world to a close. He will judge the cosmos. His claim is that he made you and that he is your Lord and your God. So if this is true—and that is the only option—then you must bow to him and worship him.

Here is a man who was meek and humble, who lived for thirty years in a village and helped his father in a carpenter's shop and yet he made these extraordinary claims. He is a colossal Christ and he does not need to brag. God does not need to boast. The Saviour is not mad. He is the most sane man the world has ever seen. He is not a wicked man pretending to be what he is not.

All of us have to face up to the fact that what Jesus said is true, that he is God, the only God there is. You will never meet a more important issue in your whole life. How do you respond? Do you bow before Jesus and say, "My Lord and my God?" Or do you listen to the boasts of others and laugh at "religion."

Are you only excited at what the unbelieving world is excited about: food and sport and entertainment? Are you just going along with everybody else as a typical drifter? If they don't think of Jesus Christ at all then neither do you.

Please listen to the teaching of the preacher of the "Sermon on the Mount." Please consider his life. Please think of the third day when he rose from the dead. This is Jesus Christ, the Son of God, who is the way the truth and the life. He is someone worthy of your life and your love, and no one else compares to him.

He lives today!

JONATHAN CHAPMAN, OR AS HE WAS BETTER KNOWN, JOHNNY APPLESEED

One of the first recorded references to Johnny Appleseed is that in 1801, in Ohio's Licking County, there is a report of him planting apple seeds and cultivating orchards. He continued doing that over the next five years though there is no record of any sightings of him until 1806 when a pioneer in Jefferson County spotted two boats lashed together on the Ohio River. The vessel was loaded with sacks of apple seeds and Johnny was sailing down the river.

Within the next couple of years this man, who came to be called "Johnny Appleseed," was known in every log cabin in all the states out West. During his journey on the Ohio River he would moor his boat at every suitable spot and go ashore with his spade and plant his rows of seeds. Then he would erect a fence around them to keep out the deer so that orchards of apple trees started to grow along the banks of the Ohio.

What do we know about Johnny Appleseed? His real name was Jonathan Chapman and he was born in Leominster near Boston, Massachusetts in 1775, where today an elementary school and also a street is named after him.

In Urbana University Ohio there is a Johnny Appleseed Museum, and in the same state there is a Johnny Appleseed Heritage Center in Ashford County. In 1966 the United States Postal Service issued a five cents stamp with his name on it.

The only surviving tree claimed to have been planted by him is on a farm in Nova, Ohio. The apples it produces are tart, hard and green, far more suitable for making cider than for munching. For this reason during the Prohibition Era in the 1920s many of the orchards Johnny had planted were cut down by the FBI so that alcoholic cider could not be made from them. The pioneer frontiersmen and women did not always have access to pure drinking water. The water had bacteria in it. So it was safer and more refreshing for them to drink a watered-down cider.

So these were the apple trees we know that Johnny planted. But how he became religious and how he came to develop this obsession with planting apple seeds which lasted over forty years is something no one knows.

We know that his father fought in the Revolutionary War at the Battle of Bunker Hill, and also worked in the defence of New York against the British Army. His father returned home unscarred from the war but around that time his mother died. His father was a gardener and those skills were planted in Johnny from his youth, but they came into sharper focus at the end of his teens when he began an apprenticeship as an orchardist. He first planted a nursery of apple trees south of Warren in Pennsylvania and then soon afterwards, around Mohican in northern Ohio. He eventually planted thousands of nurseries all over the frontier, as far west as Illinois.

Johnny Appleseed was a short wiry man, full of pent-up energy. He had long dark hair and a beard. He went barefoot in regions where one settler had killed two hundred rattlesnakes in a single year within a few acres of land. Sometimes he was given footwear, and occasionally he wore odd shoes, a boot on one foot and a moccasin on the other. One day he was given a fine pair of shoes, but when the donor met him a week later he was disappointed to see Johnny barefooted again. He argued with him, but he was told that Appleseed had met a poor sick man without shoes and he thought his need was far greater than his.

His garments were cast-off clothing, but generally he wore a coffee sack and he had holes cut in it for his head and arms to pass through. He professed to be quite happy with this. He also wore a hat made of pasteboard. The story that he wore a saucepan on his head which he also used for cooking his food is now considered to be a later embellishment.

So Johnny Appleseed became a welcomed eccentric during the almost fifty years he travelled from place to place in the American wilderness with his bags of apple seeds. He obtained these seeds from Pennsylvania's cider mills. He began by keeping them in cotton sacks, but they were not strong enough walking through dense thorny thickets. So finally he carried them in leather bags across his shoulders or on his horse. He strangely believed that it was wrong to ride a horse and so it was a pack animal he led through virgin lands. Thus he wandered through a hundred-thousand square miles of territory that consisted of forests and swamps, fording shallow rivers, pressing along narrow trails until he entered fledgling white settlements and Native American villages.

He was always welcomed, and teenagers never mocked him. His fame went before him. He carried in a bag, ribbons and calico to give to the girls. If invited to stay the night in any home he would always ask if they had enough food also to give to the children. Then he would read from the Gospels to the family. But he never stayed anywhere for very long. The Native Americans treated him kindly and spared him during the cruel wars of 1812.

Finally in 1845, on March 18 on a warm spring day, he walked twenty miles to a settlement in Allen County, Indiana. He was welcomed to stay with a family. He refused their offer of a meal but took some bread and milk which he ate sitting on the porch while he watched the sun go down and slept as usual on the floor.

In the morning when the father entered the room he found him barely conscious and later on that day he breathed his last. He was seventy-two years of age and forty-six of those years he had spent solitary, homeless, ragged, with bleeding feet, intent on making patches of the wilderness fruitful. So lived and died Johnny Appleseed.

There are two reservations we have with this extraordinary man, one far more serious than the other.

The first is that those who believe in the Lord Jesus have far better seed to sow than Johnny Appleseed had. Our seed produces much sweeter fruit than his bitter green apples. Our fruit is love, joy, peace, patience, gentleness, goodness, faithfulness, meekness and self-control. Aren't they wonderful fruits? But they can grow in your life only when the Holy Spirit takes up his home in your heart. But if you grieve the Spirit by rejecting the Word of God that the Spirit has breathed out then the possibility of such delightful Christ-like fruit vanishes. And the best you find is good manners.

Sometime in his life Jonny Appleseed came to reject the Bible's plain teaching that our heavenly Father, the Son and the Holy Spirit are all equally and fully God. He also rejected the teaching of Scripture that salvation is a gift of God to those who entrust themselves, body and soul, into who our Lord Jesus Christ is, and what he has achieved for us by his righteous life and atoning death as the Lamb of God. The Lord Jesus lived this life and died this death because of his love for repenting sinners like you and me.

Does it matter what we believe as long as we believe in Jesus Christ? Yes it does because God is very particular about what you think about him.

If you say, "Well, I think of God like this." Are you right? May we not be worshipping another image of ourselves? Our God is three persons, Father, the Son and the Holy Spirit. You had better be introduced to them now, and that comes by reading the Bible.

Think of the difference it would have made to the energy and sacrifice of Johnny Appleseed if he had gone to settlements of the American frontiers and preached the New Testament gospel to them.

He might have said, "Men and women, we deserve eternal death because of our sinful attitudes to God, but in his love he has given for our salvation his Son, Jesus Christ, that whoever puts their trust in him will not perish but have everlasting life."

Then he could have taken them through the great letters of Paul to the Romans and Ephesians and Colossians and Philippians explaining and showing them the wonderful grace of God, pleading with them to receive the Lord Jesus as their own Lord and Saviour.

This Saviour is the one who gives us a perfect and complete Scripture. We have no need of people who say that they have new words from heaven that show the Scriptures are wrong. "Your word is truth," said Jesus. So let us all look to him and know his salvation. "Believe on the Lord Jesus Christ and you will be saved."

What a message! But Johnny Appleseed did not preach that message. Instead he preached things that contradict the Bible, for example, that it was wrong to kill any living creature, even mosquitoes. It was wrong even to ride on the back of a horse. Grafting a twig onto a tree was wrong, even pruning trees was displeasing to God, and certainly it was sinful to cut down a tree.

He would take the hospitality of others who gave him food and a bath and protection through the hours of darkness, but he never could offer such hospitality to anyone else because he did not have a home. Yet, as we shall see, Johnny Appleseed was very interested in increasing his possessions.

The apostle Paul told the church in Galatia that if he (or even an angel) should preach another message other than the true gospel, then a curse should fall on him! By his false teaching Johnny Appleseed was provoking the justice of God to call down judgment on himself. So we have better seed to sow than Johnny had, seed which springs up to eternal life

The second concern is that we have better motives for sowing God's seed that Johnny Appleseed had. Why did he spend his life planting apple seeds? One reason would be that he knew the usefulness of the apple tree and wanted everyone to have a tree in the back garden so that they would rarely be without food. He loved the creation and the beautiful apple tree and that is a good thing. Its blossom in the spring and its fruit in the autumn are utterly delightful.

But there was another very powerful reason that Johnny Appleseed had for his labours: the American Government had passed a frontier law that said that anyone could claim a piece of land through developing it, and anyone could do that by planting fifty apple trees on it.

So Johnny was not like some of Lord Nelson's English admirals who, while they walked around the countryside, took a pocket of acorns and planted them so that a century later Great Britain would have English oak to build her battleships to defend the nation from invasion. Johnny Appleseed planted his seed in a nursery and built a fence around it and employed someone to look after it, and returned every year or two to see how the land had developed. Then he sold that nursery to new settlers and frontiersmen. He did this in many places and when he died he left a 1,200-acre estate to his sister.

Our motivation to sow the seed (that is the Word of God) is much better. We have been loved by the Son of God, Jesus Christ, and that saving and dying love, so amazing and so divine, demands that we give our lives and souls and indeed all that we have and are to God.

We say to God, "Take my life and let it be consecrated Lord to Thee." His love for us constrains us to be steadfast, immovable, always abounding in his work. We love our neighbours as ourselves. We have received mercy from a sin-hating God because of what the Lord Jesus has done and so we want others to know that mercy too. We live as people blessed with every spiritual blessing in Jesus Christ, and we want others to know that too. We are constrained to tell them of the friend of sinners, that he will never reject those who go to him.

So we never grow exasperated and feel defeated in this work but we wait upon God and walk on without weariness making us give up, rather we increase our speed as the years go by, finding new strength to serve God and increasingly feeling our debt to other people. We sow the seed of the Word of God and look forward to the great harvest when all God's people will be safely gathered in, free from sorrow and free from sin.

HOW A PEDLAR LEARNED ABOUT THE FINAL PRICE BEING PAID

Jack hated reading. He saw no point in it. Going to school and reading aloud to the whole class was a pain to him. So what he did was sit in front of his friend who was the best reader in the class, so that when it was his turn to read aloud and he came to a long word he slowed down and his friend whispered the word to him.

It had always worked until one day there was a word in a sentence that even his friend couldn't pronounce. When he came to it he paused like usual but his friend whispered, "Skip it!"

Jack whispered, "Eh?"

"Skip it!" said his friend again urgently.

So Jack read the sentence and when he came to the word he said, "Skip it."

The teacher seemed to be sleeping during these reading periods, or marking an exercise book, but in fact he was half listening to the class and the words "Skip it" did not seem right.

He looked up from his desk. "What's that, boy?" he asked.

Jack was silent.

"Read that sentence again."

Jack read it and got nearer and nearer to that unpronounceable word. He took a deep breath and mumbled "Skip it."

"Skip it?" said the teacher loudly, and again "Did you say 'Skip it?' Is that what you said?"

"Yes sir," said Jack as a wave of merriment ran through the whole class.

"Where in the world did you get that from?" asked the teacher. Then he pronounced the word correctly and loudly.

"Now say it. You say it."

Jack mumbled it.

"Say it again!" said the teacher.

He tried to say it again, but failed.

"Come here boy!" said the teacher picking up his stick.

And that was the end of school for Jack. He picked up his bag and walked to the door.

"Stop! Come here!" cried the teacher.

But Jack pushed the door open and slammed it behind him setting out on the three miles walk home to Washboard Creek, never to return. His days of public schooling were over. He was an absentee from any further education, a truant boy. He worked with his father on the farm and became a statistic, another lost boy without any direction in life.

One day an old Yankee pedlar came in his cart to the village and Jack was mighty impressed. The guy was good. If he were shipwrecked on a desert island he would succeed in selling maps to the island's inhabitants. He stood on his cart and greeted the gathering crowd.

Spotting a woman he cried, "My beautiful young lady, how can I help you? What can I sell you this pretty day? I've got here almost everything you have ever desired: calicoes, collars and capes from France, elegant milk jugs, pastry forks, pills for headaches and backaches and stomach aches, soothing ointments for itchy spots, essences, peppermints, winter green, measuring tapes, safety pins of all sizes, hooks and eyes, balls of wool, broaches and bangles, smelling salts if at any time you feel faint (and aren't such times ordained for all of us?), castor oil, corn-plasters, mustard, gardening seeds, silver spoons, pocket combs, teapots, songbooks, piano music, the latest hymnbooks, thimbles, slates, playing cards, baskets, wooden bowls ... Can I please you with anything today, Madam?

"And you know I have much more that that brief rehearsal of the magic cave that is my carriage, notions and potions to help you sleep or to be a real tonic to you. I have powder for your feet and shampoo for your hair, and that, by the way, comes all the way from Chicago. And after you have bought something that you need for yourself there is plenty here that your husband would like, a little birthday present or a wedding anniversary gift?"

"Do you have any goose-yokes?" asked one comedian in the crowd.

"No," replied the pedlar as quick as a flash. "There has been such a demand for them in this county that I have sold them all, so many of its discerning inhabitants wanted a dozen, but if you give me your address I will bring plenty with me next time I am passing through."

The growing crowd laughed at the repartee. Business was brisk and most people went away with something. Some took bagfuls with them, and even Jack bought something, and then the rain began to fall and the people hurried home and the pedlar took his cart to the stables next to the hotel.

That night Jack thought about the future. He wanted to see more of the world than Washboard Creek and so early next morning he went to the hotel and hung around until the pedlar came out.

"Good morning, sir," said Jack, "I am strong and honest and hard-working. I would like to offer my services to you. I believe I could be of help to you and you could certainly be of help to me. You have much to teach me and I like your style and wit. If you find me a burden or a pain in the next week or so, or if I am an inconvenience to you, then just let me know and I will go off without any bitter spirit towards you."

He had rehearsed that speech as he lay awake thinking about the future all that night.

The pedlar looked at him silently.

"You can help me feed and harness the horse," he said, "and I will think about your offer."

Jack's heart leaped within him and he worked efficiently and quickly bringing horse and carriage together, brushing down the mare, ensuring that it had had enough water.

"Then let us go," the pedlar said, and that was the

only contract of service that Jack ever got, and so simply and swiftly the next chapter in his life began.

The pedlar was getting old and a little lonely and Jack proved himself indispensable. He quickly learned the routine of his new life and soon anticipated the pedlar's needs, including learning the patter of his sales talk, until one day the pedlar was taken ill and Jack did well in a busy day's sales. The pedlar grew to love him and finally retired and left his business to Jack.

One part of his business was to run four seasonal auctions in some small towns in Louisiana. Jack watched and learned from all he saw.

He learned the chant, "One dollar bid, now two, will you give me two? Two dollars bid now three, will you give me three," and so on until the bidding stops and the item was sold.

He quickly learned to banter because sometimes the auction grew quiet, people seemed reluctant to bid, humour needed to be injected to loosen up the audience and encourage the shy to bid.

"You're not going to let him have it are you?" he would cry, or, "You have ridden all this way, you are not going to ride home disappointed?"

And then some people would think, "Okay, I will bid one more time."

He would open the auction with some tall tales, "Now how many auctioneers does it take to light a lamp?" And the answer, "Lots and lots!"

The first time Jack led an auction sale it was completely nerve-racking, but it was also brilliant and he thought, "Wow! I like this!" He learned quickly selling up to one-hundred-and-forty lots an hour in a five hour sale.

Most of all, though, he loved a roll, when two bidders both wanted to purchase an item and bid against one another higher and higher, the crowd quiet, watching, seeing who would drop out first, and then the hammer falling and sometimes there would be applause. As the towns grew and auctions were more frequent Jack branched out into cattle auctions, and finally opened a shop and became a prosperous member of the community.

He met a sweet young girl, fell in love and went to church every Sunday with her. Her pastor was very sensible and patient with Jack. He knew he couldn't force him to believe in God. He wouldn't dare pressurise him into making a decision without him having some knowledge of his need of a Saviour, or without knowing who this Saviour, Jesus Christ, was, and how beautiful he was, and why everyone needed him.

So he preached week by week and gave Jack some sermons and books by C.H. Spurgeon to read. Becoming a business man had been motive enough for Jack to overcome his disinterest in reading, and he read the literature that his pastor gave him with growing understanding.

One day they were talking together on the porch, sitting on some comfy rocking chairs, and the pastor was asking Jack about being an auctioneer, and Jack was telling him about some of his experiences and the expensive items he had sold. There was a silence and then the pastor said to him, "Yes, that is the difference between your work and mine. You have difficulty in getting people up to your price. I have difficulty in getting them down to mine."

"What do you mean?" said Jack.

"My task is making people satisfied with who the Lord Jesus Christ is, and what he has done," said the preacher. "I want them to be content with him. I want them to go to God and say to him in the words of the hymn, 'Nothing in my hands I bring, simply to Thy cross I cling.'

"Jesus is now sitting down at the right hand of God and he is completely satisfied with what he has done in his life and death. God the Father and God the Spirit are content with Jesus Christ. They want nothing more. When Christ died the only things that mattered were what Jesus had done and how God responded. Nothing else was important. Nothing else was relevant.

Everyone in heaven is satisfied with Jesus Christ, but not all the people who make up my congregation. There are too many who also want to make their own little contribution. They want to bring a little suffering, a little faithfulness, a little loyalty to the means of grace and the local church where they have been attending for twenty years, a little boldness in witnessing, a little faithfulness to marriage vows, a little generosity to the collection plate when it gets passed around and a little kindness to needy people.

"When they have personally added those things then they think that the work that Christ has done will be perfect, when they have made their personal contribution of what they have accomplished in their lives then they will get to heaven, they think. They are not satisfied with who Jesus is and what Jesus has done.

"But the problem is that everything we have done is imperfect; it is mixed with sin. Before God it doesn't pass muster. It is like a china vase that you would sell for a good price if it were not so chipped and cracked. It is like the silver ornaments you try to sell for a high price, but they are dented and damaged. They are less than perfect. Do you see, Jack, that these people are not able to say, 'Nothing in my hands I bring, simply to Thy cross I cling?'

"So you see what I am saying Jack? You want people to come to your auction with their hands full of money to buy what you are selling. I want people to come to my pulpit with empty hands, poor in spirit, surveying the wondrous cross where the Prince of Glory showed his love for them by taking all their guilt and blame so that they could be forgiven. They run to him for refuge and don't take refuge in what they have done. We bring nothing but our sin and need and he gives us everything."

This was a powerful moment in Jack's life. It was a moment of light and truth that changed his whole relationship with God, and his whole understanding of Jesus Christ. It is a lesson that every single person needs to learn. We must all go the way the illiterate boy called Jack went, how he came with nothing to the one who is all in all.

THE HUNTED GOOSE

An old African American told this story many years ago. There was once a handsome goose who loved to swim up and down the lake. There was a little island right at its heart where she had her nest, safe from wolves and foxes.

So, her happy years passed, respected by all the ducks and voles and water rats who lived around the lake. She didn't bother anyone and no one bothered her ... except for Mr. Fox who loved nothing more than the taste of goose.

He wandered around the shore, a deeply frustrated animal, running from tree to tree to get close to Mrs. Goose, but she could see his every movement and refused to let him get near to her.

He once tied a dead fish on a line and threw it out

where it floated on the surface of the lake and he jerked the line once or twice to make it look like it was alive. He thought that the goose would swallow it, line and all, and he could pull the dead fish to the shore, goose and all.

But Mrs. Goose could see that the fish was old and dead and the line was there on the surface of the lake.

Poor old Mr. Fox. He is desperate to have me, she thought, and so she was very careful.

The months went by and then Mr. Fox had an idea. He tied some planks of wood together and made a little raft. Then he lay on it and paddled through the reeds at one end of the lake hiding amongst the bulrushes where Mrs. Goose came to devour the frogs that lived among them. He lay there motionless for ages as she busied herself hunting tadpoles. She came nearer and nearer to where Mr. Fox lay on his raft. And then she paddled right up to him, only looking down for frogs and tadpoles. Then ... Splash!

"I gotcha!" shouted Mr. Fox in triumph as he grabbed her beautiful long neck and pulled her onto the raft.

What terror and shock she experienced as he snarled at her and, with his legs, paddled the vessel through the reeds to the shore. He caught her up under his arms and held her neck strongly, laughing in triumph.

"Now, Mr. Fox," said Mrs. Goose when she had regained her composure, "you think very carefully of what you are doing. I have as much right to this lake as you do. We can live together in respect and peace. This is as much my lake as it is yours. We will have to take this matter to the courthouse and let the judge decide whether you have any right to grab me like this and kill me and eat me."

That stopped Mr. Fox smiling. He knew of the F.A.C.J., the Forest Animals Court of Justice, and its powers. But he also reassured himself as he remembered who were its officers.

So a week's later Mr. Fox and Mrs. Goose appeared in court. But when Mrs. Goose sat down and looked around, her heart sank. The officials on duty were foxes, the clerks of court were foxes, the attorneys for the defence as well as for the prosecution were both foxes, the twelve on the jury were also foxes, the judge himself was a fox, and the large audience who had come to hear the case were almost all foxes.

These were the ones trying and passing judgment on Mrs. Goose, and it's unsurprising to know that the court convicted her, finding her guilty, wrapping it up in a few long words and one or two in Latin.

When she was given an opportunity to speak she faced the judge and said to him slowly and deliberately, "As a ring of gold in a swine's snout so is a beautiful woman who lacks discretion."

The judge heard, blinked, and understood her criticism of his biased verdict.

Then they took her outside to finish her off and they got the big oven heated up ready to cook her. But then there was a strange noise in the sky. Looking up they saw a great flock of geese, scores and scores of them, like weighty hurtling arrows, in a V shaped squadron diving down upon them singing:

> "Welcome beloved friend, welcome we cry.
> Come with us on our journey through the sky."

And down they swooped scattering all the foxes, and with a great smile and a loud honk of delight, up, up and far away Mrs. Goose flew joining them in their flight to life and freedom.

When all those folk in the courthouse were foxes, and you are just a common goose then there isn't going to be much justice for you is there? And so it had been for African Americans, for in fact he was telling the story of many of his ancestors.

He remembered, as they all did, the cruelties, injustices and discriminations that had happened. Though he was also very glad that things were slowly getting better.

How we hate to hear of such discriminating and racial sinfulness. Some ignorant and nasty people think one race—their race—is superior to everyone else's. So there is harassment, and victimisation, and a lack of opportunity. How horrible it is.

God has told us that after we die there is going to be a very fine evaluation of how each of us has lived our lives. It will be a perfectly fair occasion. It will not be a loaded court full of bias without any possibility of a just and true verdict of "Not Guilty." God knows everything and he will bring every factor into consideration, the privileges we enjoyed or did not enjoy, the opportunities given to us or not, the encouragements or discouragements, the rewards or the punishments, the knowledge or the ignorance that was ours.

Some children are raised in the most loving homes where God is honoured and obeyed. Other children are raised in homes where Jesus Christ is scorned. It will be more tolerable for them when Jesus judges the world than for those who learned of his love from the beginning of their lives but rejected it. More will be required of those who have known a great many privileges.

But the judgment will be absolutely straight. There will not be a single miscarriage of justice. Every mouth will be stopped. No one will think, let alone complain, "This is horribly unfair. This court is run by the foxes, and so I am lost."

The psalmist looked forward to this great day of cosmic justice, saying that all of creation will "shout for joy before the LORD, for he is coming ... to judge the earth. He will judge the world with righteousness and the peoples with his faithfulness" (Psalm 96:13). During their lives many people have been like poor Mrs. Goose facing a trial in which everyone is biased against them. The people in power all wanted her dead and there was no possibility of justice. Not in that great coming day. Our judgment will be from the most loving and merciful judge in all the universe.

In this world there is terrible cruelty and destruction of old and young. Men and women get away with their terrible actions. No one is punished for them. The wicked grow rich and those who have lost their sons and daughters, wives and husbands, break their hearts and grieve for a long time. They long for justice, that those who did such evil should be properly dealt with. They certainly will be! This is a moral universe. We will all have to answer to our Creator for what we have done.

So when we go to church we are often going to hear about this great day, just as Paul spoke to the people of Athens and said to them that God "has set a day when he is going to judge the world in righteousness by the man he has appointed. He has provided proof of this to everyone by raising him from the dead" (Acts 17:31).

So what are we to do? Jesus Christ was asked, "What must we do to perform the works of God?" This is the answer of our Lord, "This is the work of God—that you believe in the one he has sent" (John 6:29).

Was the Lord Jesus Christ a wicked man? Was he cruel? Did he tell lies? Did he frighten people unnecessarily? Did he abuse women or children? Was he selfish? Was he greedy? Did he make promises and never keep them?

There was never a wiser or kinder man on the face of the earth.

And what power he had over creation, over evil, over disease and death! What a teacher he was!

Is there another speech that can compare to Jesus Christ's "Sermon on the Mount?"

So is it surprising that God desires every one of us to entrust ourselves into the safe keeping of Jesus? If you do trust him then there is absolutely no possibility that God will condemn you because you are united to and protected by him.

THE LEGENDARY CASEY JONES

In the first half of the twentieth century small boys were asked what they wanted to be when they grew up. The traditional reply in the United Kingdom was, "An engine driver." But in the United States the answer was, "An engineer."

The same thing is called two different names. It is the job of driving trains across the countryside and in and out of big towns and pulling on the whistle that announces its approach. But the job is given a different title each side of the Atlantic ocean.

There were no famous engine drivers in Great Britain, though there were famous engines like the Flying Scotsman, but in America there one famous engineer and his name was Casey Jones.

He was born in 1864 in the state of Missouri. His

father was a schoolteacher and he had great ambitions for his son. He gave him the name John Luther Jones, after the writer of the fourth Gospel and the great German reformer Martin Luther.

Not long after his birth they moved to the town of Cayce in Kentucky. He moved from there at the age of fifteen to his first job in the bigger city of Columbus and his fellow workers named him after the place he had just left, "Casey" Jones they called him, and the name stuck.

He got a job as a telegrapher for the Mobile and Ohio Railroad. Soon he was promoted to the position of railroad flagman in Jackson, Tennessee, where he met a pretty girl named Janie Brady.

When he was twenty-two years old they married and soon they had a family. Five years after they were married he became an engineer on the Illinois Central Railroad.

Casey Jones was quickly recognised as one of the best engineers in America. He got the trains that he drove to their destinations right on time. He never let the passengers down. He was so punctual that people said they could adjust their watches to the time his trains pulled into the station. He generally drove between Jackson, Tennessee and Water Valley, Mississippi. But he also endeared himself to his passengers and the farms he passed through on his journeys in another way, by the sound he got out of the train whistle.

These were special whistles made out of six thin tubes of different sizes. When Casey pulled on the whistle's rope he made a long drawn-out sound. It began softly, and then it rose to full volume and then died away softly to a whisper. That sound became his trademark. People in bed on a farm near the railroad would hear this haunting sound as the train approached a road which was crossing the railroad, and a husband would say to his wife, "There goes Casey Jones." It was famously described as a "whippoorwill call."

He moved from being a freight train driver to a passenger driver in an interesting way. He was the driver appointed by the World's Fair when it came to Chicago in 1893. All through that summer he shuttled thousands of visitors from Van Buren Street Station to Jackson Park where the World's Columbian Exposition was being held. People would stop by and thank him and ask him questions about the locomotive. He enjoyed all this personal contact and soon afterwards applied for a job driving passenger trains.

At the World's Fair one of the exhibits on display

was a magnificent new engine with eight drive wheels and two pilot wheels, the 2-8-0 Consolidation Class. Casey drove it on the 589 mile journey to Water Valley, and until he transferred to Memphis in 1900 he continued to drive it.

Then Casey went on to drive the biggest and fastest train in the south. This was Engine 382 known as "Cannonball." It was steam driven, a ten wheeler with six huge wheels six feet high. The fireman who worked with him and kept the coal feeding the flames was his friend John Wesley McKinnie. There they were, Luther and Wesley, or better known as Casey and John. They had some adventures together.

One day the train was approaching Michigan City, Mississippi, and Casey went out on the running board of the locomotive to oil the relief valves. He finished the job and returned to the cab before they reached Michigan City Station, but as he looked ahead he saw a group of children in front of the train on the track. He pulled the rope of the whistle and to his relief they all jumped off the railway line, except for one little girl who was petrified with fear and rooted to the spot as the train came nearer and nearer.

"Put it in reverse," he shouted to John, his fireman.

Without taking a breath Casey leaned out of the

door and shouted at the top of his voice, "Get off the line!"

But the girl was frozen, scared stiff, gazing at the train getting nearer and nearer.

Casey got out of the cab and moved quickly along the running board of the locomotive once again, right to the very front of the train. He climbed down and stood behind the cowcatcher and leaned out over it, his arms stretched out and out, as far as he could reach. Just as the train was about to hit, he grabbed firmly and lifted her up while the train went slowly rolling on finally to stop. Casey held her close, weak with relief. He had saved her life.

Late on April 30, 1900 one of the engineers was taken ill and Casey volunteered to drive the train instead of him. The journey was from Memphis southwards to Canton, Mississippi. Sim Webb was his fireman and they left Memphis at 1 a.m., thirty minutes late. So Casey ran the locomotive at speeds of over eighty miles-per-hour to make up the time. He made up almost all the late time and said to Sim with a smile, "Sim, the old girl's got her dancing slippers on tonight."

All was safe, although it was a foggy night, until the track circled around a big bend in Vaughan, Mississippi. The curve blocked Casey's view of the railroad ahead but Sim Webb suddenly saw that there was another train on the track ahead of them. An air hose had broken and four carriages were still on their line unable to move.

Sim shouted the danger at Casey who grabbed the brake with one hand and pulled the whistle with the other to warn anyone surrounding the stationary freight train of their approach.

He cried to Sim as they got nearer, "Jump off! Jump off!" while doing all he could to slow down the train.

Sim jumped off about three-hundred feet before impact and knocked himself out as he hit the ground. There was a brutal collision at thirty-five miles-per-hour, with the caboose of the stalled train full of hay, then another carriage full of corn, and another full of timber. Then Casey's locomotive left the rails and ploughed into an embankment where it overturned and was completely wrecked.

One of the passengers resting in his sleeper that night was Adam Hauser, and he wrote about his experience.

"The passengers did not suffer. There was no panic. I was jarred a little in my bunk, but when fairly awake the train had stopped and everything was still.

Engineer Jones did a wonderful as well as a heroic piece of work, at the cost of his life."

The only casualty was Casey Jones himself, who was crushed by the crash. His watch stopped at that moment of impact, 3:32 a.m.

For the next ten years the wrecked train lay there and sightseers drove to view it. But the locomotive was finally repaired and ran again, in fact until 1935.

The scattered corn actually grew for years afterwards in the surrounding field. Fireman Sim told the story of the crash until his death in 1957. And in the following year, Casey's wife Janie died aged ninety-two. She received $3,000 in insurance payments and compensation. She wore black nearly every day for the rest of her life. Casey is buried in Mount Calvary Cemetery in Jackson, Tennessee and some railway enthusiasts erected a tombstone to mark his grave in 1947.

Casey's fame was spread and sustained by a song that was made famous by the country singer Johnny Cash. A fellow railwayman named Wallace Saunders wrote the words and tune called "The Ballad of Casey Jones."

A movie was made in the early years of Hollywood in 1927 about him, and there was an annotated cartoon made by Walt Disney in 1950. In Water Valley, Mississippi, there is the Casey Jones Railroad Museum. Casey's name is synonymous with America's steam era. He stayed at his post. He wanted others to live and was prepared to give his own life that they might be saved, and he succeeded even though he died.

The Lord Jesus Christ spoke about a similar thing. He said that no man has greater love than to lay down his life for his friends.

Casey Jones felt a great obligation to the people who had entrusted themselves to his care. They had paid the price of their tickets and they had climbed up onto the train that he was driving. They sat there and they thanked him if ever they bumped into him at the end of the journey. He had safely brought them home.

It was very rare for Casey to know any of the passengers personally, though he did know the firemen he worked with and was concerned on the night he crashed that Sim did not die.

It was different for the Lord Jesus when he saved us from death. He knew us personally, every one of us. His Father had given us to him. He entrusted us to him, saving and keeping us. Our Lord gladly took the responsibility of taking care of us. He was determined that we would not perish but have everlasting life. There was nothing about any of us that he did not know, all our kind actions as well as all the bad things that we have done. He was determined that he would lose none of the billions of people God his Father had given to him and he loved each of them, just as the Father and the Spirit of God also loved them.

All of them had broken the law of God. They had failed to love God with all their hearts. They had not loved their neighbours as themselves. They did not want to go to heaven and enjoy the presence and the joys of eternal life with a holy God. They loved themselves and wanted to please themselves in everything they did. They kept God out of their lives but God kept loving them, and Jesus kept loving them, and the Holy Spirit kept loving them. He stirred people to pray for them. Through these people he brought them to hear the gospel of the love of God in Jesus Christ. As they heard the Word he illuminated their minds so that they understood the message and saw their need of believing in Christ. He overcame their doubts that they were not good enough and would not go on to live a true Christian life. He gave them a new birth and they understood the wonderful love of Jesus Christ, that he had become the Lamb of God and he had laid down his life that they might live. He had given his life for their sins. He had taken away their guilt that they might not perish but have everlasting life.

"I died, so that they will not die."

Just like Casey Jones. He did not abandon the train, jumping off the locomotive and leaving all the passengers to a grisly fate. He stayed there, refusing to leave his position, becoming the one who took all the danger and death so that none of those he cared about perished. That night they all lived, but Casey died. People realised this afterwards talking of Casey Jones and saying, "He did a wonderful, heroic piece at the cost of his life."

So it was that the Lord Christ gave his life that we could be spared. Jesus was good, and righteous, and loving towards us. We did not grasp until much later that he was such a brave young Saviour who was prepared to die that we might live, but that is the meaning of the cross of Calvary. He would not give up on us, and escape from his terrible death. He would not ask for a thousand angels to take him home and abandon us. Through giving his life in his death we get eternal life as his gift.

FIRE, FIRE, FIRE!

It had been a busy day for Farmer Bill. He had supervised the work in the cotton fields from the time the sun rose until it set. He was glad to get on his horse and ride home. His wife had made him one of his favourite meals: fried chicken and turnip greens. Then he had a good long bath and finally he climbed the stairs, put on his pyjamas and went to bed.

Bill was falling asleep when his wife came into the bedroom carrying their little boy Sonny.

"Everything okay?" he asked his wife Lou Ann.

"He won't sleep and he says that he wants to talk with you."

"Yes?" said Bill. "What's wrong?"

Sonny clung to his mother and whispered in her ear.

"You tell him."

"No, you tell him."

Then more giggling.

"Hi, Father."

"Hi, Sonny. How are you doing?"

"Good, Father."

Then there was a pause and more whispering, and finally Lou Ann came over to the bed.

"What's all this about?" Bill said.

"Oh, Sonny can't sleep and he wants you to sing the fire song to him."

"What?"

"The fire song. You sang it to him. You taught it to him. You sang it when you were a boy and he loves it, but no one can sing it like you, and after you have sung it then he says he'll sleep. Sorry!"

"Oh, that's okay. Imagine he likes that one song! It's certainly not because of its deep theology! Sure, I'll sing it to him. Are you ready Sonny?"

"Sure," came a quiet voice.

Farmer Bill began a bit huskily:

> *"One thing we need O Lord,*
> *One thing we want today*
> *The church is cold and dying*
> *So hear us while we pray for,*

Fire, fire fire! Fire, fire fire!"

He shouted out the last six words.

"Again," said Sonny.

"Well you must join in and sing it with me," said Bill. Then he sang it again:

> *"One thing we need O Lord,*
> *One thing we want today*
> *The church is cold and dying*
> *So hear us while we pray for,*
> *Fire, fire fire! Fire, fire fire!"*

"Again," said Sonny, and they sang it again and again each time louder and louder, shouting out the last six words as the children in Junior Church would shout out the last words at the top of their voices.

"Thanks so much Bill," said Lou Ann. "Now I can put him to bed. Say good night and God bless to your father."

Sonny did and Farmer Bill slipped under the duvet again.

Bill's bedroom was at the back of the house and he barely heard the fire truck as it hurtled up the track to their farmhouse. He never heard the horse's hooves or the rumble of the wheels or the clanging of the fire truck bell, but he certainly heard the thunderous knocking on the front door, and he jumped out of bed and ran down to open it. There stood two uniformed firefighters, stern and very sober.

"There is a fire in your farmhouse?"

"Is there?" said Bill.

"Abraham works for you, doesn't he? He came breathless to the fire house five minutes ago telling us that he heard you calling again and again 'Fire, fire, fire!' and he did not stay for a moment even to put his shoes on but came running barefoot to us and hammered on the door and told us about the fire. He even helped us harness the horse to the fire truck and then came running behind us as we came here as fast as we could. For what? A false alarm? What's going on? Who's fooling around. Abraham is a good man and so are you Bill. We knew each other in Yazoo City School. Did Abraham hear the shouts from another farm? Have you been drinking? That's not like you. You're not a drinking man. What do I write down in my report book for today? What sort of false alarm is this?"

Bill hung his head and blushed.

The firefighter hadn't finished.

"Do you know, sir, that we cannot refuse to answer a call for firefighters especially when it comes during the cotton harvest. What if the fire spreads to a cotton field? Do you know that at this very time there may be a fire somewhere and we are far away dealing with a false alarm?"

Farmer Bill wanted the floor to open up and swallow him.

"Oh dear! I am so sorry. Oh dear ... oh dear."

"What's this all about, sir?" said the fireman. "You know that it's an offence to call for a fire crew to come out with all our equipment when there's no fire?"

"Oh dear," said Bill again. "Oh, how embarrassing. I'm so sorry."

"What happened?" asked the firefighter. "I have to send in a report."

"I was singing," said Bill.

"Sinning?" asked the firefighter.

"No, not sinning. I was singing."

"Singing?" asked the officer frowning, not fully understanding what Bill was saying.

"My wife came up to the bedroom. I had been up since five and have got to be up early tomorrow morning for the harvest. But our boy Sonny couldn't sleep, and he wanted me to sing to him. There is a song I've sung to him, a fun song that the children sing in our church and it's about fire."

"About fire?" said the fireman.

"Yep," said Bill. "I'd better sing it to you:

> *"One thing we need O Lord,*
> *One thing we want today*
> *The church is cold and dying*
> *So hear us while we pray for,*
> *Fire, fire fire! Fire, fire fire!"*

"But we sing it louder than that, in fact all the children shout out 'Fire, fire, fire!' very loudly, and they stamp their feet. So that is what I sang to Sonny to encourage him to sleep. It was not to wake up the firefighters of Yazoo City and bring them here with the horse and the other men on their horses and cause a false alarm. I am so sorry. I guess that Abraham was in bed over the stable and he heard me shouting and ran for you. He's a good man. I never thought ... I am sorry ... so sorry."

"I understand," said the firefighter. "But I happen to go to Second Presbyterian Church every Sunday and I have never heard of that song."

"Maybe they don't sing it because you are there," said Bill, getting a bit more confident as the firefighter had relaxed.

"Maybe," the officer said. "But what in the world are you singing about?"

"I don't think it is very helpful," said Bill, "in fact I don't like it. I wish we didn't sing it in First Baptist, I wish my son had never learned it. I wish I had never sung it to him. I don't think I will ever be able to sing it again."

"But what's the point of the song?" asked the fire marshal. "Why sing about fire? Have you heard the news of prairie fires and forest fires and all the animals those fires kill, millions of them and the homes and crops and people destroyed? Why in the world would you teach children to sing for fire? To ask God for fire?"

The officer shook his head in confusion.

Bill said, "I think the man who brought the song to our church, the music director, grew up in the Salvation Army and the motto of the Salvation Army is 'Blood and Fire.' That comes from the Day of Pentecost in Acts. Do you know that?

"The Holy Spirit was poured out on the church and tongues of fire rested on every disciple. They were not harmful burning flames. They were signs of the Holy Spirit of God coming upon each of them. When men live and speak in the living power of God then they are like John the Baptist. You know he is described as a burning and shining light. The fire is a sign of the power of the Holy Spirit destroying sin and giving light and warmth to cold lives spent in darkness."

Bill got excited as he spoke and he began preaching to the fire marshal.

"That is what the children sang about, or should be singing about—if they knew what they were singing, 'Fire, fire, fire!'"

"That is very interesting," said the firefighter captain. "There is a lot of show and form and outward behaviour in our churches. Maybe it's that fire we all need, or should I say that I need."

"I certainly need it," Bill added, and then another word of apology.

The fireman replied, "I can see now why there was this misunderstanding. That's okay, I don't think you will hear from us again."

"No, and you won't hear from me either, and I don't think Abraham and his family will be hearing me singing 'Fire, fire, fire!' again. And I would like to give you a contribution to the work you do fighting fires, and I hope you get no more calls this week or through the harvest time."

"Oh there is no need," said the captain.

"No way!" said Farmer Bill and he gave him ten dollars.

With thanks the two firefighters turned away

waved goodbye and they went back at a more sedate pace to the fire station. Bill did not sleep for a long time, but then in the days ahead he often prayed for the captain whom he had met, so unexpectedly, at his front door, and their conversation. But whenever they sang another song it brought back memories of that night and the fire truck coming to the farm, and he shook his head with embarrassment and sighed.

Purify us from within send the fire today.
To burn up every trace of sin send the fire
    today
To bring the light and glory in,
The great revival now begin,
A real deep longing now instill,
Send the fire today. Send the fire today.

THE REMARKABLE STORY OF POCAHONTAS

When we were young we used to play "Cowboys and Indians." When we got a little older, we saw Hollywood movies about the battles between those two groups. Today, though, there is sadness and guilt about how Native Americans were treated by the first settlers. In the midst of that history is a moving story about a young Native American girl called Pocahontas.

She was born in 1595 and was the daughter of Chief Powhatan the leader of Tsenacommacah, a Native American tribe that lived in what is now called Virginia. She was given the official name of a chief's daughter, Amonute, when she was born but as she grew up she displayed such a happy and confident nature that her family and friends called her Pocahontas, which means "delightful playfulness."

She was favoured as the chief's daughter, but he expected her to do what all the other women did: growing crops, learning to cook, gathering herbs, building a home, curing skins, tanning hides to make moccasins and clothes, butchering meat and so on. Hard, but rewarding and satisfying work. She also visited the English fort at Jamestown and played with the children there. She would turn cartwheels with them.

The English settlers arrived in May 1607 under the leadership of Captain John Smith. Tensions developed between the Native Americans and the English and it was not long before another of Chief Powhatan's children took John Smith prisoner. They took him to meet the Chief and forced him down on the ground then put his head on two stones. Another man took a large rock and raised it above his head as if he was going to strike Smith with it, but Pocahontas ran forward, knelt down and put her head on the head of Captain Smith to protect him.

Historians disagree about whether the Native Americans were really planning to kill John Smith or if they were just playing mind-games with him, but either way Smith was relieved that no harm was done to him.

For some time John Smith was held as a prisoner by Powhatan and we have evidence that during those months he taught Pocahontas some English and she taught him her tribal language. Ultimately the Chief and the Captain bartered, and Smith was sent on his way. John Smith could never forget the spontaneous action of Pocahontas in protecting him even if his life had actually not been in danger.

As Pocahontas grew into her teens she used her favouritism with her father to help the English settlers. They struggled planting their first crops and she arranged for food to be brought to them.

She was also the negotiator when some of the English were taken prisoner when she was thirteen. There was continued tension between the two nations and by 1609 it was doubtful whether the colonists could survive. Disease, starvation and poverty weakened and decimated their numbers and they were increasingly dependent on the Native Americans to survive. The English were resentful and threatened to burn down the homes of the Powhatan tribes if they were not sold more food and there were sessions of hard bargaining.

Many Native Americans were angry with these interlopers and their demands, and spoke of attacking them and killing John Smith, but Pocahontas heard of these plans and warned the English and saved their lives. Smith was injured in some sort of gunpowder explosion and he was taken on a ship and went back to London, but Pocahontas and the tribes were told that he had died.

Finally a war broke out between the English and the Native Americans and Pocahontas could do nothing to make peace between the two sides. In fact, she was kidnapped when she went onto a English ship and the captain sent a message to Chief Powhatan that he could have his daughter back if he released some English prisoners, and returned stolen weapons, and sent the colonists some food. But the Chief sent only half of what had been agreed and left her in the hands of the English.

She was taken to a settlement called Henricus and a minister of the gospel, Alexander Whitaker, was given the task of being her teacher. He taught her to speak English, and to learn the Scriptures. He presented her with the life of the Lord Jesus Christ. He told her that every single person, no matter their race or background, was guilty before God. But most of all, he explained the wonderful love of God that showed itself in his goodness and patience to his rebellious creatures.

The Lord Creator has spoken to us not only through our consciences and the order and glory of creation, but also through his servants the prophets until, in the fullness of time, he came into the world in the person of his Son Jesus Christ. He was the true and perfect man. He obeyed and loved God and he loved his neighbour as he loved himself. Finally he became the Lamb of God to whom God imputed our sin, judging and condemning our guilt in him as the sin-bearer. God now summons us to repent of our sins and to entrust ourselves to Jesus. He promises that all who do this will not perish but have everlasting life.

So Pocahontas learned more and more about the Bible and one day she told her pastor, Alexander Whitaker, that she had asked God to forgive her sins and that Jesus had become her Lord and Saviour. He rejoiced at the news and she was then baptised and she was given another name, "Rebecca."

In the next months in Henricus she met another Christian named John Rolfe. He had lost his wife, Sarah, and their child in Bermuda after they sailed to America and now he was a lonely farmer and had asked God to give him a new family. He asked her father, Chief Powhatan, for the hand of his daughter in marriage and he consented. It was unusual for a coloniser to marry a Native American and so he also had to ask the English governor, Thomas Dale. The governor gave his permission and so in April 1614 John Rolfe and Pocahontas were married, and that helped to bring some peace to the region and an end to armed hostilities.

Two years later a ship was sailing to England. The Virginia Company of London, who ran the colony, needed more financial support. They believed they could create more interest in what was happening in America if Londoners could see some of the Native Americans, and especially Pocahontas and her husband with their new baby boy, Thomas. So a dozen Native Americans sailed to England with Pocahontas and her husband and son. The ship arrived at Plymouth and the family journeyed to London.

It was a triumphant time for Pocahontas. She was esteemed as a princess and introduced as Lady Rebecca Wolfe. She went to church and to plays and was presented to the royal family. Then one day to her astonishment she heard that the man she thought was dead, Captain John Smith, was alive and she met him. She was overwhelmed with emotion thinking of her action as a little girl in putting herself over him to protect him when she thought he was going to have his brains dashed out. She referred to him as "Father" which he found embarrassing, but she also rebuked him for the way he had treated her people. He then wrote to the royal family about Pocahontas and urged that people in London treat her with respect.

The Virginia Company decided to have a portrait of her made dressed in fashionable clothes. Beneath the portrait the words were written, "Matoaka, alias Rebecca, daughter of the most powerful prince of the Powhatan Empire of Virginia." This is the only image of her we have.

After a year, Pocahontas, John Rolfe and their son, Thomas, set sail to return home to Virginia, but they had hardly gone down the Thames river when she became very ill and had to be taken ashore in Gravesend. It is not known what disease she had picked up but there in Gravesend she died. She had put her hope in the God of grace and she said to John, "We must all die. It is enough for me that my son lives."

She was buried at St. George's Church in Gravesend on March 21, 1617. A life-sized bronze statue of her stands in the graveyard today. John Rolfe went on to Virginia but their son Thomas remained with his father's relatives in England where he stayed for twenty years before he also went to Virginia and received his inheritance. He became a successful land owner and farmer. He married Jane Poythress and their daughter was born in Virginia. She in turn had six grandchildren, and so many famous Americans have since claimed to be among Pocahontas' descendants. In 1907 Pocahontas was the first Native American to appear on a U.S. stamp.

In Massachusetts, forty-five years after Pocahontas' death, John Eliot began to translate the Bible into the native Natick language. It was the first Bible printed in North America. In the following century David Brainerd evangelised the Native Americans in Delaware and saw God save many of them. His brother John continued the work after David's death and carried on until he passed away in 1781. Jonathan Edwards, the greatest American theologian, spent six years of his life preaching to a congregation containing mainly Housatonic Native Americans. Since that time, God has raised up many missionaries to translate Scripture and teach it to thousands of Native Americans.

THE ROBIN AND THE BEAR

It was a freezing winter. The snow came early and it stayed and stayed. The first week was fun. The children loved making snowmen, having snowball fights, making sledges and sliding down the hills, but as week followed week it got colder and colder. There was less and less food to eat. All the logs they had gathered in the summer were being burned up and the fires started to go out. There were no warm drinks, no soup and everyone was aching for a hot meal. Chewing cold strips of venison three times a day was so boring.

One by one the fires in the wigwams began to go out and the children cried, and the mothers turned to their husbands and said to them, "Do something. Light a fire!"

But the husbands sighed, "We don't have a flame to light it with, not even a spark and there is little wood left."

The great ugly mountain bear watched and heard all of this, and he was mighty glad. "Now they'll move from my valleys and my canyons, my hills and my forests and leave them to me, and again I will be the king here."

The little animals trembled when they heard that, but they were so weak. None of them could resist the mighty black bear. But the brown breasted robin was a plucky little bird and did not give in so easily. He feared the reign of the black bear. That animal could climb the trees and pull apart the nests of all the birds and eat the chicks. What power would be his alone if all the Native Americans moved away from this area! The bear was afraid of them with their rifles and bows and arrows.

But what could a little robin do in the midst of this great freeze? It could easily have given up saying, "I am a nobody without strength, unable to do a thing to help." But it didn't.

Maybe I will cheer them up by singing all my favourite summer songs to them, it thought.

So it started, perched on a bough on the edge of the village it sang its best, but a robin is not a nightingale. It does not have a melody or much of a range, and none of the people of the village noticed. They were all too cold.

"What can I do? I don't want a takeover by Bear."

It longed for the spring and long days and the summer sun.

Why do we choose to live so far north? it thought.

The robin knew that in the south the snow did not cover the land, and the Native Americans who lived there were still cooking and keeping themselves warm.

"Ah! I will go there, and bring back the fire," he decided and off he flew.

It was a long way, but the further south he went the warmer the sun shone, and before it grew dark he arrived in a village beyond the snow. He found a safe tree and a hole where a squirrel had once lived, and there were some nuts and insects to eat in the shelter of the hours of darkness.

The next morning he cautiously flew around the camp and saw the fires burning and smelled the food cooking. He noticed a bush near a fire and darted across the clearing and perched there. Then there was a twig that had fallen out of the fire, and it was smouldering on the earth. No one was there and so the robin darted across and picked up the end in its beak and up and up he flew and across to the beginning of the snow fields, and then on and on further and further north, at times holding the twig under one wing and gliding with the other wing. Very clever. What a clever bird! But it was so relieved to see its home village deep in the snow and the cut out pathways, with chest high walls, that went from one wigwam to another.

The robin had thought of a clump of rocks and some dry grass, as the best place to start a fire. There were some twigs and branches already there, and so it settled on the boulders and put the smouldering branch safely in the cleft of a rock. The brown breasted robin picked up the dead grass and put it on top of the twig and beat its wing so that a tiny breeze made it flare up and light the grass, and then the robin picked up all the twigs it could find and soon there was a fire!

"They will come. The men will come, and soon there will be fires in the wigwams."

And sure enough someone soon came, but it was the big black bear growling its hatred and kicking the fire to pieces.

The robin flew round and round the bear's head squawking out its anger at the bear that simply swung its paws in a vain attempt to kill the robin.

The robin saw all its work was in vain and sighed and perched on a tree.

But the next day before dawn he flew off again to the edge of the snowfields and on south to the village where the women were preparing food for their families. He now knew what to do, perching in the midst of the bush, its beady eyes watching everything, waiting for some burning twigs to fall to the earth.

It finally happened, and darting across, carefully picking it up, off he went again flying back through the snow on the long journey back to his village. There were already dead twigs around the rock from the previous day and plenty of dead grass and he started a fire again.

Very soon someone noticed it, but it was not a Native American, it was not a man or woman or a child. What was it? Yes, it was the big black bear, kicking out with both its feet and swinging away with its paws until the fire was out again.

Right, thought the robin, if you want a war then a war you are going to get!

It went to its shelter and ate its food and slept and early the next day off it flew all the way out of the snowfields to the sunnier south, waiting in the bush for ages until a burning twig fell from the fire, swooping across the earth and carefully picking it up, then flying back on the long journey, soaring, gliding, sheltering the little flame with increasing expertise until it came to the snowy, freezing village.

There was no better spot for a fire than the cluster of rocks and now there were scattered around from two former fires dry grass and twigs and soon he had a fire going.

"Tweet, tweet tweet!" it cried wanting the villagers to come out and see the flames and smoke, but the only living creature to come lumbering up to the little fire was the big black bear who smashed and scattered the newly lit bonfire. "Another battle lost," the robin said to itself, "But I am going to win this war, not this big bullying bear."

The next day it flew the familiar long journey south and finally picked up a smouldering twig and flew back. This time it placed the smouldering twig in the rock cleft and then flew around the wigwams singing, crying and squawking from one home to another until he heard voices.

"Can you hear that bird? What's wrong with it? It hasn't been trilling away like that for ages. Go and see! Go and see!"

Then the robin flew back to the twig, but it seemed to have gone out and he stood by its side very close and fanned and fanned the twig with its wings.

Nothing seemed to be happening, but he would not stop and then one little flame appeared and he dropped some dry grass on it that flared up. Then he dropped a twig on that, and another on that and another and another and another. Then the robin heard voices, not growls of anger, but human voices. Out of the corner of his eye he saw the bear lurking behind the trees but afraid to come nearer because some of the men were carrying their Winchester 45s.

"Fire!" they all shouted with joy.

Men and women, boys and girls came out of the wigwams at that magic word and along the channels cut through the snow and ran to the clump of rocks.

"There's fire! We've got fire!"

Immediately they picked up any wood and fed the flames and soon they carried burning branches back to their wigwams to melt snow and make hot water and hot food.

"The fire has come! Fire has returned!" they shouted.

They did not ask how. Only one woman saw an exhausted robin lying on the snow, and she picked it up and carried it back to her home and put it to warm near her new fire. In the light of the fire she noticed something very strange, that its breast was not brown, as it had been, but red, and from that time onwards all robins were known as robin redbreasts. In fact, nobody knows when there was a time when they were all brown-breasted or that there had been a change that came about through the thoughtfulness and kindness of the first robin redbreast.

———

Of course, this is a legend. It did not really happen any more than what we read of in the Bible in the book of Judges about trees talking and asking the olive tree to be their king.

Still, it is a fable that gives us a wonderful message of truth.

We are little people but we must never give up. The world is dark and cold. There is not a lot of warmth, but we must never say, "I am nobody. I am nothing. I could not bring light and warmth to anybody's life."

If you are a Christian then you have energy in your heart that comes from heaven, and just like the little robin, you can trust in the Lord and ask him for help and mount up with wings like an eagle and fly without growing weary. You can carry a flaming torch of light and warmth and fire that changes the lives of others.

You can do much good through Jesus Christ helping you.

The devil, like a vicious and hateful bear, wants to destroy the lives of those in whose hearts God lives. The nasty bear is the god of this world, but there is a greater one whose name is Jesus and through him you, like the little robin, can destroy the mighty bear and bring light and warmth to those who have been living in the cold darkness of unbelief.

Do not be afraid. Do not think that you are too small to do anything. Let your light shine! Let your warmth spread today! Be brave.

Ask God to help you say to yourself, "I can do all things through Christ who strengthens me."

REFORMATION LIGHTNING

We are a micro publisher specialising in creative
Christian writing for young readers.

Discover more at ReformationLightning.com